HORRIBLE

NOW A MAJOR CBBC TV SERIES

WAS ROME BUILT IN A DAY?

FRIGHTFULLY FUNNY QUIZ BOOK

TERRY DEARY ILLUSTRATED BY MARTIN BROWN

SCHOLASTIC

Scholastic Children's Books,
Euston House, 24 Eversholt Street,
London, NW1 1DB, UK

A division of Scholastic Ltd
London ~ New York ~ Toronto ~ Sydney ~ Auckland
Mexico City ~ New Delhi ~ Hong Kong

Published in the UK by Scholastic Ltd, 2010

Text copyright © Terry Deary, 1993–2009
Illustrations © Martin Brown, 1993–2009

Some of the material in this book has been previously published in:
Horrible Histories: The Massive Millennium Quiz Book and The Awesome Ancient Quiz Book

All rights reserved

ISBN 978 1407 11747 8

Printed and bound by Bookmarque Ltd, Croydon

2 4 6 8 10 9 7 5 3 1

The right of Terry Deary and Martin Brown to be identified as the author and illustrator of this work respectively has been asserted by
them in accordance with the Copyright, Designs and Patents Act, 1988.

CONTENTS

HORRIBLE HOMINID HABITS

Human ancestors were a strange bunch and no mistake, but then, life was hard for hominids – they had no TV, no microwaves, no MP3 players (no school either, though, so maybe it wasn't so bad). They had to fight daily dangers just to survive. How would you get on in prehistoric times? Take this quick quiz and find out.

1 How did early Stone Age hunters trap a delicious woolly mammoth for their tea?
a) By cornering it in a cave
b) By stampeding it into a swamp
c) By tempting it with a teacake

2 How did Stone Age people go into a trance to talk with their dead ancestors?
a) By starving themselves
b) By eating a type of fungus
c) By holding their breath until they turned blue

3 What was trepanning?
a) Drilling a hole in someone's skull while they were alive
b) Dancing in a circle around a fire
c) Skinning a bison with a flint

4 What did Stone Age people wear?
a) Thermal knickers (it was cold in the Ice Age)
b) Animal skins
c) Woven leaves

5 What is a barrow?
a) A Stone Age device with one wheel, used for carrying dead animals
b) A Stone Age farming tribe
c) A Stone Age burial place

6 What weapons did Stone Age hunters use?
a) Flint axes
b) Machine guns
c) Wooden swords

7 What did prehistoric people use to draw on cave walls?
a) Brushes made of animal hair and juice from different fruit
b) Their fingers, flint and soft clay
c) Paint and a padded roller

8 How did Stone Age chefs cook up a feast?
a) Throw an animal in the fire – fur, feathers and all
b) Order takeaway from the pizza cave around the corner
c) Skin an animal then cook it in a clay pot over a fire

EXTRAORDINARY EVIDENCE

Archaeologists have learned all sorts of fascinating facts about life in the Stone Age just from studying the bones and stones they have discovered. Some things are strange but true, others are prehistoric porky-pies. Can you tell which is which?

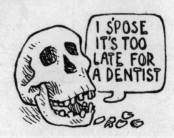

1 There were dentists around in Stone Age times.

2 Stone Age people lived alone, hunting and gathering for themselves.

3 Neanderthals – relations of early humans – were known to track and kill small dinosaurs.

4 Even cavemen liked to look good, and shaved or plucked their body hair.

5 Some Stone Age people may have slit open the stomachs of animals and helped themselves to the creature's last meal.

6 Stone Age people believed in a god they called Homo Sapiens Rulus.

7 Some of the stones used to make Stonehenge were carried from a site in Wales nearly 400 kilometres away.

8 Nasty Neanderthals collected human heads, which they'd smash open to remove the brains.

AWFUL ANCESTORS AND ROTTEN RELATIONS

Archaeologists have given some tongue-twisterish names to our early relations. See if you can figure out what each of these lunatic Latin names actually means. (The pictures below should help you out…)

1 Homo sapiens sapiens
2 Homo ergaster
3 Homo erectus
4 Homo habilis
5 Homo neanderthalensis
6 Homo rhodesiensis
7 Homo sapiens
8 Homo rudolfensis

a) Handy human
b) Lake Turkana man
c) Wise human
d) Working human
e) Rhodesian human
f) Wise wise human
g) Neander Valley human
h) Upright human

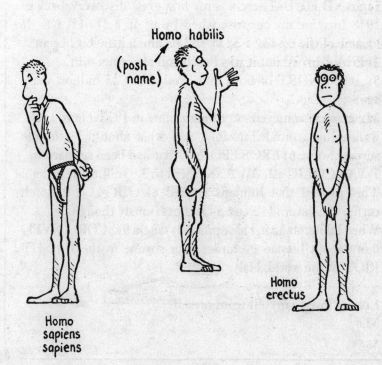

Homo habilis
(posh name)

Homo
sapiens
sapiens

Homo
erectus

THE LOOPY LEAKEYS

Louis Leakey and his wife Mary were two of the most famous anthropologists (that's the posh name for someone who studies ancient humans) that ever lived. Mary in particular made some amazing discoveries. Here is what she might have written in her diary, looking back at a lifetime spent sweating in the sun to uncover the secrets of strange Stone-Agers. See if you can unscramble the words in capitals.

Dear Diary,

Well, I have certainly proved that I am the most awesome anthropologist ever – loads better than my hominid-hunting 1) SAND HUB. There was my first great discovery, back in 1948 Imagine my surprise when I dug up a 2) SULLK. It looked a little bit like a 3) MANUH and a little bit like an 4) PEA. Turned out it was Proconsul africanus – an 5) ACE SNORT of both that lived about 25 million years ago!

My greatest achievement though came in 1978 There I was, wandering around Tanzania, and what should I stumble across? Some 6) FROSTPOINT that had been set hard in 7) VANCOLIC ash. We dated them to 3.5 million years ago! This proved that humans walked 8) GIRTH UP much earlier than stupid scientists had previously thought.

When I think about it, I have probably taught 9) SCOREDIVED more about human evolution than anyone in the 10) SHY RIOT of the world. Ha!

Lots of love to myself from myself.
Mary
xxxx

AWFUL EGYPTIANS

EXTRAORDINARY ANCIENT EGYPT

How would you fare in the wacky world of ancient Egypt? Take this quick quiz and find out if you're clever enough to be worshipped as a fearful pharaoh or so stupid you'd be set to work as a slave.

1 How might Ancient Egyptians treat a nasty cut?
a) Strap a piece of fresh meat to it
b) Smear it with horse dung
c) Chop off the injured finger/arm/head

2 How did pharaoh Pepi II keep flies away from him?
a) He invented the first fly spray using cat urine
b) He had his slaves covered in honey so the flies would buzz off towards them
c) He ordered his army to kill all flies

3 How did ancient Egyptian embalmers remove the brain from dead pharaohs?
a) They stuck a hook up the nose and pulled the brain out through the nostrils
b) They sliced open the top of the head and removed the brain with a special spoon
c) They sucked it out through the ears using a straw

4 What does the pharaoh Ramesses' name mean?
a) 'Re has chosen him'
b) 'Re has finished him'
c) 'Re has sneezed on him'

5 The ancient Egyptians were crazy about cats. How did they mourn their mangy moggies when they died?

a) They wore black for a month

b) They sacrificed mice at a statue of the cat

c) They shaved off their eyebrows

6 What was the name of the ancient Egyptian book of prayers used to protect against evil spirits?

a) 101 Ways to Protect Against Evil Spirits

b) The Dangerous Book for Mummies

c) Book of the Dead

7 How were gruesome grave robbers punished?

a) They were impaled on a sharp stick

b) They were buried alive in the grave they robbed

c) They were beheaded with an axe

8 According to legend, how did Cleopatra, the last queen of Egypt, die?

a) She was strangled by a snake

b) She was bitten by a snake

c) She was murdered and fed to a snake

GROOVY GODS

The ancient Egyptian gods were a confusing crew – they took all sorts of names and shapes and they were all in charge of different areas of life (and death). Some of the greatest and ghastliest gods introduce themselves below. Can you work out who's who?

1 Don't be fooled by my beetle-like body. I might roll around in poo (or roll poo around), but I'm actually the sun-god reborn, which makes me pretty powerful. (Or should that be poo-erful?)

2 I'm a cow-headed lady who loves a good time – the goddess of music, dance and drinking. So if you fancy grooving with the gods, pop round to my place for a bit of a party.

3 You might say I'm the unluckiest of the gods – murdered by my brother, chopped into pieces and scattered to the four winds. Luckily my wife Isis managed to find most bits of me and stick me back together again, but I'm a bit green from the experience.

4 I might look like a monkey (or maybe a frog), but you don't want to monkey around with me – I'm the king of the gods, an all-powerful almighty.

5 If you fancy a spot of bother I'm the god to see – the lord of chaos and evil. Trouble is my middle name. If you want to know how murderous I am, just ask my brother Osiris…

 **6** I hold the power of (after)life and death in my hands. Come and see me and we'll have a good heart to heart… Actually I'll put your heart on my scales and decide if it's weighed down with wickedness or as light as a feather.

7 I'm the school swot in the world of the gods – lord of wisdom and writing. I might look like a baboon, but I'm no boob…

 **8** You might have seen pictures of me – I'm the one with the head of a hawk wearing a funny hat. Despite my dubious dress sense, I'm a powerful god, in charge of the king and kids.

So, can you match who's who?
a) Osiris, **b)** Anubis, **c)** Seth, **d)** Hathor, **e)** Horus, **f)** Thoth, **g)** Khepri, **h)** Amun

EGYPTIAN FACT OR FICTION

While the rest of the world was wandering around in animal skins and using basic stone tools, our Egyptian friends were reading, writing and ruling an awesome civilization. Can you work out which of the following facts about these ancient experts are true and which are just mad myths?

EEK

1 The first workers ever to go on strike were in ancient Egypt.

2 The ancient Egyptians counted how many they had killed after a battle by chopping off the heads of their dead enemies.

3 Scissors were invented by the ancient Egyptians.

4 Ancient Egyptian doctors believed they could cure toothache by placing a dead mouse in the patient's mouth.

5 Some of the Kush kings from Sudan had their rotten relatives buried with them when they died.

6 The Egyptians were the first people to make toffee apples.

7 It took around 25,000 slaves five years to build just one pyramid.

8 The best ancient Egyptian soldiers weren't sent to fight wars, they were used to guard the pharaoh's palace.

BARMY EMBALMING

Below is a page from the secret diary of an Egyptian embalmer. Unfortunately it's so very ancient that some of the words have faded away. Fill in the gaps to make sense of the mad method of mummification.

Dear Diary,

Well we finally finished mummifying the old pharaoh yesterday, so he's good and ready for the 1)_____. It's a disgusting job being an embalmer, I can tell you. To begin with, he was pretty stinky, so we took him to a special tent to blow away the fumes. When he was a bit less pongy we started work. First we pulled out his 2)_____ (by way of his nose) and packed the empty space with 3)_____ to stop it rotting. Next we ripped out his liver, stomach, intestines and lungs. Sounds brutal, but don't worry, we stored them carefully in 4)_____ in case he needs them later. We left the 5)_____ where it was, of course. He'll be wanting that. After the body had been properly pickled in salt, it was looking a bit shrivelled and empty, so we stuffed it with 6)_____ to plump it up a bit. He looked more like his old self then, so we wrapped him in 7)_____. All that was left to do was to pop him in his 8)_____ and wish him bon voyage. Hope he makes it to the next world – he was a pretty nice fellow (as pharaohs go).

a) canopic jars, b) brain, c) linen, d) sarcophagus, e) natron,
f) heart, g) afterlife, h) bandages

PHASCINATING PHARAOH PHACTS

The kings of Egypt ruled for nearly 3,000 years, so the history books are filled with facts about pharaohs. Some were cruel and some were clueless. Some lived long and prospered and others died dastardly deaths at the hands of assassins. Here are some curious questions about the most famous of these ruthless rulers...

1 Where did Pharaoh Khufu build his pyramid? (Clue: he was a greedy geezer)

2 What was stuffed up Ramesses II's nose when he was being mummified? (Clue: he must have sneezed all the way to the afterlife)

3 How did Pharaoh Amenemhet's tomb-makers try to stop grave robbers pillaging his pyramid? (Clue: you'll be amazed)

4 What did the female pharaoh Hatshepsut wear to make her look more like a man? (Clue: it was a hairy disguise)

5 How did Ramesses III punish the judges who went to parties with the people who plotted to kill him? (Clue: they didn't get a fair hearing!)

6 What is Pharaoh Pepi II most famous for? (Clue: long live the king!)

7 Who did Amenhotep III take as his wife? (Clue: keep it in the family)

8 What did Pharaoh Narmer do to his enemies? (Clue: he showed them who was head honcho)

GRUESOME GODS

Most awesome Egyptian myths have various versions of the same story. Here is one version of the Isis and Osiris story. Sadly our suffering scribe has scrambled the terrible tale in places! Can you unscramble the words in capitals? (It's easy – about as easy as unscrambling a scrambled egg!)

Osiris was a popular feller – for a king, that is. His people loved him! Of course someone hated him – his brother, Set, who was very up-Set. Slimy Set was jealous of popular Osiris and plotted against him. Set secretly got his brother's measurements and had a MAGNETIC FIN casket made to fit. This casket was in the form of a human-shaped box.

Sneaky Set then IN DOG'S EAR a large feast. Seedy Set invited Osiris and 72 others. At the height of the IF IT IS STEVE Set produced the casket and ACNE DO NUN that it would be given to whoever it fitted. All the guests tried the casket for size, but none fitted until finally Osiris stepped into the casket. (What a mug!)

Set (who was not a mug) immediately slammed the lid closed and sealed the casket shut (with boiling lead). The SAD LEE coffin was then thrown into the Nile.

Isis was upset at the loss of her husband and SHE CARED for the casket all over Egypt. At last she found it where it had come to rest in the roots of a huge tree.

Isis took the coffin back for a proper ALI RUB. For safety she hid it in the marshes beside the Nile. Unfortunately for Isis, Set found the casket while he was out hunting and was so ENRAGED he chopped the body of Osiris into pieces, and RESTED CAT the parts throughout the land of Egypt.

Poor Isis had to then set out again looking for the bits of her husband. At last she found all the parts except one (his naughty bit) and SMEARS BLEED Osiris and wrapped him in bandages. The first mummy!

He was also a daddy and his son, Horus, went out to battle his savage uncle Set. After a series of battles neither was able to win. In the end Osiris was made king of the underworld, Horus king of the living, and Set ruler of the deserts as the god of evil. So they all died happy ever after!

WROTTEN WRITING

The Egyptians invented writing. They needed it to keep count of all their wealth! They invented the 'picture-writing' that we call *hieroglyphics*.

Now see if you can read this message – remember, the sound of the letters is more important than the English spelling.

A. vulture
B. leg
D. hand
F. viper
G. pot or stand
CH. rope
I. reed
J. serpent
K. basket
L. lion
M. owl
N. water
P. stool
Q. hill
R. mouth
S. cloth
T. loaf
W. chick
Y. reeds
Z. bolt

Now see if you can read this message – remember, the sound of the letters is more important than the English spelling.

POTTY PYRAMIDS

They are H-U-G-E. The pyramids were built as graves for the pharaohs after they left this life. They were filled with goodies so the kings would be as rich in the next life as they were in this life.

Of course they've all been robbed now – some were robbed at the time of the burial and the rest have been cleaned out by greedy treasure-hunters in the twentieth century. (They said they were collecting historical material for our education. That's a bit like a bank robber saying his hobby is collecting bank notes … they are all just robbers!)

Not everyone agrees the pyramids are graves, of course. Thinking about those great lumps of dense stone, are people with great lumps of dense brain who have other ideas. But which of the following wacky ideas have some people seriously believed? Answer true or false…

Someone has said that the pyramids are…

1 Adverts. The priests wanted to leave something to show the world how great they were.

2 Simple landmarks. All maps would be drawn with the pyramids at the centre and distances worked out from there.

3 Chambers of horrors. Dead kings were stuck inside, then the Egyptian people were charged two onions an hour to walk around and view their kingly corpses.

4 Sundials. The shadow from the Great Pyramid would be used to work out the time.

5 Fortune-telling machines. They've been used to predict the birth of Christ, the date of the First World War and the end of the world – AD 2979 if you're worried.

6 Star calculators. They help to measure the speed of light, the distances from the earth to the sun and to keep a record of the movement of the stars.

7 Calendars. They can measure the length of a year to three decimal places.

8 Star maps. The pyramids are laid out in the same pattern as a cluster of stars called Orion. Of course you could only see this pattern if you are ten miles up in the air – or a Martian in a flying saucer.

9 Centres of invisible forces of the universe. Weird things can happen there – like blunt razors turning sharp and people feeling wobbly at the knees when they enter.

10 Maths calculators. Take the distances around the edges and the angles and whatnot and you can work out the distance round a circle (its circumference) if you know the distance across (its diameter).

Quick Egyptian Quiz

1 The Egyptians made houses from bricks. The bricks were made from mud mixed with straw or something else. What? (Clue: not to be sniffed at)

2 Pilgrims came to ancient Egypt like holidaymakers to Blackpool. What miniature mummies did they buy as souvenirs? (Clue: did they have to kill these creatures nine times?)

3 A weaver who took a day off work would be punished. How? (Clue: you can't beat it)

4 Priests shaved off all their hair and eyebrows. Why? (Clue: not such a lousy idea)

5 Egyptian gods were often pictured with animal heads. Hapy had a baboon's head and Qebehsenuef had a falcon's. But Pharaoh Horemheb was buried with a rare god who had what sort of head? (Clue: flipping tortoise!)

6 The god Khnum created the first Egyptian people. What did the Egyptians believe he made them from? (Clue: they were earthy people)

7 Farmers scattered corn on their fields. How did they trample the seed in so the birds couldn't eat it all? (Clue: they were seen and herd)

8 Another way to keep birds off crops was to use scarecrows. These scarecrows were better than modern ones as they could run around screaming! How? (Clue: you must be kidding)

9 After reigning 30 years a pharaoh would have to prove his strength. How? (Clue: it was a good idea in the long run)

10 How many sides does an Egyptian pyramid have? (Clue: slightly sneaky)

ROTTEN ROMANS

EVIL EMPERORS

It's really weird but true. Some of the battiest people in history have been leaders – kings and queens, emperors and empresses, presidents and princes. It's almost as if you have to be slightly potty to be a ruler!

Rome had their fair share of rotten rulers. Here are a few foul facts about them. Only the odd word has been left out for you to complete…

Here are the missing words, in the wrong order: mother, head, chicken, horse, corpse, cobweb, cheese, wife, wrinkly, leg.

1 AUGUSTUS CAESAR (31 BC–AD 14) CAUGHT BRUTUS, THE MURDERER OF JULIUS CAESAR, AND HAD HIS _____ THROWN AT THE FEET OF CAESAR'S STATUE.

2 TIBERIUS (AD 14–37) SAID THAT HE WOULD SMASH THE _____ OF ANYONE WHO DISOBEYED HIM.

3 CALIGULA (AD 37–41) WANTED SOMEONE TO HELP HIM TO RULE SO HE GAVE THE JOB TO HIS _____ .

4 CLAUDIUS (AD 41–54) HAD HIS _____ EXECUTED.

5 NERO (AD 54–68) TRIED TO DROWN HIS _____ .

6 VITELLIUS (AD 69) HAD HIS _____ THROWN IN THE RIVER TIBER AT ROME.

7 HADRIAN (AD 117–138) FORCED A _____ TO COMMIT SUICIDE.

8 ANTONIUS (AD 138–161) DIED OF EATING TOO MUCH _____ .

9 ELIOGABALUS (AD 218–222) HAD THE CURIOUS HOBBY OF COLLECTING EVERY _____ HE COULD FIND.

10 HONORIUS (AD 395–423) HAD A _____ CALLED 'ROME'.

Stabbing Jules

Julius Caesar was a brilliant Roman leader, but he became a bit too big for his boots – his red boots, in fact. The Romans were now used to having leaders who were 'elected'. They had hated their old kings … who had worn red boots instead of a crown, but when the booted-up kings were kicked out the Romans got on much better with their elected leaders.

But Julius got himself elected for life. Just like a king. When he started wearing red boots, his number was up. There was just one way to get rid of him then – assassination.

His friend Brutus led the murderers, who struck when Caesar was entering the Roman parliament (the senate). Roman writer Plutarch told the gory story. Can you sort out the scrambled words in this version?

Some of Brutus's gang slipped behind Caesar's chair while others came to meet him. Cimber grabbed Caesar's robe and pulled it from his neck. This was the A SLING for the attack.

Casca struck the first blow. His IF KEN made a wound in ASS ACRE neck but Caesar was able to turn round, grab the knife and hold on. The HAT CREWS were horrified but didn't dare move or make a sound.

Each AS SINS AS bared his dagger now. They pushed Caesar this way and that like a wild BE SAT surrounded by hunters.

Brutus stabbed Caesar in the groin. Above all Caesar had RED TUTS Brutus. When he saw Brutus coming towards him he pulled his robe over his head and sank down.

The attackers pushed Caesar against the ASTUTE of his old enemy Pompey. The statue became drenched with DO LOB.

Caesar received 23 wounds. Many of the assassins WON DUDE each other as they fought to stick so many knives into one body.

FOUL ROMAN FOOD

Do you know what the rotten Romans ate? Have a go at this quirky quiz on cuisine (that's a posh word for 'cooking') and find out…

1 The Romans didn't have tomato ketchup but they did have sauce made from what?

a) sheep eyeballs
b) fish guts
c) elephant's tail

2 At posh Roman feasts guests ate more than their stomachs could hold. How?
a) They emptied their stomachs by vomiting every now and then.
b) They stretched their stomachs with special exercises.
c) They stuck a pin in their stomach to let out trapped air and let in more food.

3 Snails were fattened up before they were killed. They were kept in a bowl of what?
a) chopped cabbage
b) brains
c) blood

4 Emperor Eliogabalus also served a meal where the peas were mixed with what?
a) queues
b) poison
c) gold nuggets

5 Emperor Eliogabalus served 600 of them at one feast. What?
a) ostrich brains
b) ducks' feet
c) camel burgers

6 A Roman called Trimalchio had a feast with a roasted boar. When it was sliced down the belly, what came out?
a) maggots
b) songbirds
c) a dancing girl

7 What could you watch as you ate at some Roman feasts?
a) television
b) two gladiators trying to murder one another
c) tap–dancing bears

8 The Romans ate cute little pets that you probably wouldn't eat. What?
a) cats
b) budgies
c) dormice

9 The Romans did not eat animals' what?
a) teeth
b) brains
c) lungs

10 Emperor Maximian was a strange eater. Why?
a) He was the only vegetarian emperor.
b) He ate only eggs and drank only water.
c) He ate 20 kilos of meat a day.

AWFUL ARMY

The Romans were famous for their army. They were well organized and well armed. They were also mainly foreigners. The conquered peoples around the empire joined the Roman army and conquered other peoples who joined the Roman army and conquered ... and so on until they ran out of conkers.

But how much of the terrible truth do you know about these super soldiers?1 If you were a beaten tribesman but refused to fight in the Roman army what could happen to you?

1 If you were a beaten tribesman but refused to fight in the Roman army what could happen to you?
a) You would be forced to do all the washing up for the Roman army.
b) You would have your hair cut off so everyone could see you were a coward.
c) You would have your head cut off so everyone could see what happened to trouble-makers.

2 What did the Roman soldier wear under his leather kilt?
a) nothing
b) a fig leaf
c) underpants

3 Who paid for a soldier's
food, uniform, weapons ... and burial?
a) The emperor paid for everything.
b) The general paid for his soldiers out of his wages.
c) The soldier paid for himself out of his wages.

4 If you joined the Roman army how long did you have to stay in it?

a) 3 years

b) 25 years

c) 40 years

5 What would you use instead of toilet paper in the army toilets?

a) your underpants

b) a sponge on a stick

c) your sword

6 Who could a Roman soldier marry?

a) no one

b) a slave

c) a Roman

7 How tall did you have to be to be a Roman soldier?

a) under 1.6 metres

b) between 1.6 and 1.8 metres

c) over 1.8 metres

8 Roman spear-heads snapped off when they hit something. Why?

a) They were made of rubbish British iron.

b) The Romans made them to break off.

c) They weren't real spears, they were just for show.

GORY GLADIATORS

A Roman writer said…

> *Gladiators were men who fought with swords in the amphitheatre and other places for the amusement of the Roman people.*

Another Roman writer, Seneca, went to see the Roman 'games' and wrote…

I HAPPENED TO DROP IN ON THE MIDDAY SPORT IN THE ARENA. I WAS LOOKING FOR A LITTLE (1) _____ BUT SAW ONLY (2) _____, PURE AND SIMPLE. THE FIGHTERS HAVE NOTHING TO PROTECT THEM. THEIR BODIES ARE OPEN TO EVERY BLOW, AND EVERY BLOW FINDS ITS MARK. THEY ARE LASHED FORWARD SO THEY CAN'T ESCAPE THE (3) _____.

IN THE MORNING MEN FIGHT (4) _____ AND BEARS, AT NOON THEY FIGHT EACH OTHER. THE (5) _____ FIGHT AGAIN AND AGAIN UNTIL THEY ARE DEFEATED. (6) _____ IS THE FIGHTER'S ONLY WAY OUT. THE (7) _____ SAY, 'BUT THESE MEN ARE HIGHWAY (8) _____ AND (9) _____. THEY DESERVE ALL THEY ARE GETTING!' CAN'T YOU SEE HOW WRONG THIS (10) _____ IS?

Missing words, not in the correct order: butchery, lions, death, robbers, sport, entertainment, murderers, spectators, winners, swords.

Seneca was banned from Rome for eight years for daring to say that about Emperor Caligula's sport! (Don't feel too sorry for Seneca – he was not a nice man!)

Quick Roman Quiz

Why not pester your parents and find out how much they know about the rotten Romans with this quick quiz?

1 In AD 64 Rome had a great fire. Emperor Nero blamed the Christians. How did he punish them? (Clue: let the punishment fit the crime!)

2 Why were there no dead bodies in Rome? Well, not for more than a couple of days. (Clue: they weren't buried in the dead centre of Rome)

3 Roman kids used a bit of a pig for a ball. What bit did they use? (Clue: a load of tripe)

4 If a gladiator fell but wasn't quite dead then a servant finished him off. How? (Clue: that's hitting the nail on the head)

5 A poisonous Roman spider bites you. You crush its body into the wound to cure it. But what do you use if you can't catch the spider? (Clue: search the internet)

6 The Romans cut off Saint Alban's head for being a Christian. As Alban's head hit the ground the executioner clutched at his own eyes. Why? (Clue: that's what you do when pupils fall out)

7 In AD 71 Spartacus led a slave rebellion. It ended when 6,000 slaves were executed along the side of a road. How did they die? (Clue: they were very cross.)

8 Chariot races were between four teams – reds, greens, blues and whites. They often caused fights to break out. Who fought? (Clue: too easy to need a clue!)

MEASLY
MIDDLE AGES

Middle Ages Mind-Benders

A muddled monk wrote these facts about the Middle Ages. But he jumbled the words and he added one word to each sentence that doesn't belong there! Can you sort the words into the right order? (Clue: the odd word out is always in the same position in the sentence)

KNOW HOW YOU HARD WHEN IT'S NOT REALLY TROUT

1 Brides threw over the guests sawdust wedding cake.

2 Teachers were allowed to stab their students not Mondays.

3 A rider road and drowned his horse in a hole in the head.

4 An umbrella used his foot as a giant single snail.

5 The Count of Armagnac broke his bones in a wife's row boat.

6 A pantry looked panter after the castle crumbled.

7 Walter Tyler's proper rebel name was Wat luck.

8 Barrel boys' at St Paul's school collected a pee in the teachers hats.

9 Heads polished their stone with a monks habit.

10 Calais Dick Whittington was twice mayor of London.

Clueless Cures

The people of the 1300s didn't know how to cure the plague but made some weird guesses. Which of the following did they actually try?

1 Sniff scented flowers.
2 Kill all the town's cats and dogs.
3 Wear a magpie's beak around your neck.
4 Build huge bonfires in the street to burn the bad air.
5 Drill a hole in your head to let out evil spirits.
6 Don't drink from any well because it could be poisoned.
7 Sleep on your side because sleeping on your back lets foul air run into your nose.
8 Drink cream mixed with the blood from a black cat's tail.
9 Eat onions, leeks and garlic.
10 Eat ten-year-old treacle mixed with marigold flowers and powdered egg.
11 Stop having baths or shaves or a change of clothes.
12 Run away to the countryside where the air is fresh.
13 Throw sweet-smelling herbs on a fire to clean the air.
14 Sit in a sewer so the bad air of the plague is driven off by the worse air of the drains.

PERHAPS THE PLAGUE'S NOT SO BAD AFTER ALL

15 Swallow powders of crushed emeralds.
16 Eat arsenic powder.
17 Try letting blood out of your body (when your horoscope is right).
18 Shave a live chicken's bottom and strap it to the plague sore.
19 March from town to town flogging yourself with a whip to drive out devils.

WEIRD WORDS

Books began to be printed in English and people could read the horrible sufferings of the peasants – though the peasants themselves probably wouldn't have been able to read. William Langland wrote a poem about a peasant called 'Piers Ploughman' and his miserable life. Can you work out just how miserable from this part of the poem? Some of the words have been scrambled by a careless printer – well, the first book printed in English was produced in 1475, so he hadn't had a lot of practice.

The Peasant

> *His coat of a cloth that is NITH (1) as the East wind,*
> *His DOHO (2) full of holes with his HARI (3)*
>   *sticking through,*
> *His clumsy HOSSE (4), knobbled and nailed over*
>   *thickly,*
> *Yet his SOTE (5) poked clean through as he trod on*
>   *the ground.*
> *Two miserable mittens made out of old GRAS (6),*
> *The fingers worn out and the FHLIT (7) caked on*
>   *them,*
> *He waded in mud almost up to his KLANSE (8),*
> *In front are four NOXE (9), so weary and feeble*
> *Their BRIS (10) could be counted, so wretched they were.*

QUICK MIDDLE AGES QUIZ

1 In 1301 King Edward I's son, Edward, was proclaimed a prince. But he wasn't proclaimed Prince of England. Instead he was named prince of where? (Clue: not the Prince of Dolphins)

2 Edward I brought law and order to England. How did they say he dealt with a leading outlaw who was robbing travellers? (Clue: king of the road)

3 In 1314 the Scots were still fighting the new English king, Edward II. Scot James Douglas captured Roxburgh castle with a trick. What? (Clue: hide in places!)

4 In 1337 Edward III claimed to be King of France. The French disagreed and the Hundred Years War started. How long did it last? (Clue: not a hundred years!)

5 In 1376 Edward III died and ten-year-old Richard II was crowned the following year. He walked into Westminster but was carried out. Why? (Clue: zzzzz)

6 One of the curious rumours that was going around was that Richard II was born without what? (Clue: you can have sausages like this, but not humans)

7 In 1381 Richard's government charged an unpopular 'Poll Tax' of four pence for every person. A rebellion was led by a man called Tyler. What was his first name? (Clue: yes, it is!)

8 The end of the century brought the end for Richard II. In September 1399 he was forced to give up his throne to Henry IV. If he burst into tears then something he had invented would come in useful. What? (Clue: who nose if he really did invent it?)

9 The 1400s were just six days old when Richard II died. He had been a prisoner of the new king, Henry IV. How did Richard die? (Clue: he has no stomach for a fight)

10 Henry V took the throne in 1413 and married Catherine. Two hundred and thirty years later the writer Samuel Pepys kissed her. How? (Clue: everyone likes a kiss from their mummy)

11 Henry VI sat at the head of his parliament. But he sat where no English king has sat before or since. Where? (Clue: another kiss from mummy)

TERRIBLE TUDORS

QUICK TUDOR QUIZ

This was the age when the Tudor family brought terror to Britain. Brit sailors discovered new worlds and new ways to kill themselves – like tobacco – while Tudor Tower torturers found new ways to make you suffer. Even queenly necks were on the block while Henry's fat bum was on the throne.

1 In 1502 King James IV of Scotland fell in love with Margaret Drummond, but she died suddenly. What curious thing happened to her sister at the same time? (Clue: double trouble)

2 Henry VIII came to the throne in 1509. Two people had to die so he could become king. Who? (Clue: father and son)

3 In the 1514 Battle of Flodden between England and Scotland, the Earl of Surrey was carried into battle. Why? (Clue: no zimmer frames)

4 Queen Catherine was in charge of England when her army beat the Scots at Flodden because Henry VIII was in France. The Scottish king was hacked down. What gruesome gift did Catherine send Henry to celebrate the win? (Clue: James would be chilly without it)

5 In 1528 the Protestant Scottish rebel Patrick Hamilton was executed. Why was the damp weather bad news for poor Pat? (Clue: smoking is bad for your health)

6 In 1532 a cook, Richard Rosse, poisoned 17 people with his soup. He should have been hanged but Henry VIII

thought of a more suitable way to execute a killer cook. What? (Clue: one for the pot)

7 In 1534 a fortune teller, the Holy Maid of Kent, said that Henry VIII would 'die a villain's death' if he married Anne Boleyn. Henry made sure that the Maid died a villain's death. How? (Clue: knot good)

8 In 1535 Henry's friend Thomas More was beheaded for opposing the king. Thomas warned the executioner about his neck. He said, 'Be careful because it's...' What? (Clue: no giraffe)

9 In 1536 Catherine of Aragon died and she was buried in a plain grave. But in Victorian times a group of ladies clubbed together to buy her a marble gravestone. What did they have in common with the dead queen? (Clue: not called Aragon)

10 In 1536 Queen Anne Boleyn was beheaded but not a drop of blood was spilled on the block? Why not? (Clue: someone swipes Anne's head!)

11 On 4 January 1540 Henry VIII was due to marry wife no. 4, Anne of Cleves, but he put it off for two days. Why? (Clue: you might do this with homework!)

12 In 1541 Henry headed off to York to meet the Scottish king, James V. What did James do that made Henry furious? (Clue: stand up?)

13 In 1541 the old Countess of Pole went to the block as unusual. How? (Clue: catch me if you can)

14 In 1542 Henry had wife no. 5, Catherine Howard, executed for having boyfriends while she was married to him. He also executed Lady Rochford, Cathy's housekeeper. For what? (Clue: Cupid?)

15 In 1545 Henry VIII went to watch his magnificent warship, the Mary Rose, set sail to sort out the French. What did Mary Rose do to surprise the king? (Clue: behaves in a fishy manner)

16 In September 1546 Henry VIII was very ill. His doctors knew he was dying but they didn't tell him. Why not? (Clue: look what happened to the Holy Maid of Kent)

17 Henry VIII had his dinner delivered to his sick room on 31 January 1547, as he had done for the past month. What was so odd about this delivery? (Clue: he had no appetite)

18 Henry was buried in his huge coffin. There is a gruesome story that Catholic daughter Mary had his corpse dug up. Then what? (Clue: the first of many)

19 Edward VI came to the throne in 1547 Ed's pet dog warned him of a mysterious night-time visitor. What happened to the hero mutt? (Clue: it was a shot in the dark)

AWFUL AZTECS

In 1519 the Spaniards arrived in Mexico and met the Aztecs. These people made the Tudors look like harmless hamsters. Apart from their horrible habit of human sacrifice, how much do you know about the Aztecs? Answer true or false.

1 Aztec warriors wore metal armour.
2 Aztec princes cut out the hearts of sacrifice victims with a glass knife.
3 Boys were trained to be warriors and were given battle dress when they were still babies.
4 Aztec warriors believed they would become hummingbirds if they died in battle.
5 The Aztecs had public toilets.
6 Warriors with long hair were seen as the best fighters.
7 Aztecs liked to eat scum.
8 An Aztec boy had to ask his best friend for permission to get married.
9 Young Aztec men could be made full warriors by having their faces smeared with the blood of a heart that was still beating.
10 The Spanish caught terrible diseases from the Aztec people.

HORRIBLE HENRY

Henry VIII was one of Britain's cruellest monarchs ever. Here's a quick quiz to test your brains. Get one wrong and your head goes on the block…

THAT'S WHAT YOU GET WHEN YOU TAKE ON A TUDOR!

1 When wife no. 1, Catherine of Aragon, died Henry had a…?
a) ball
b) fight
c) cup of tea

2 Wife no. 2, Anne Boleyn, needed the toilet a lot during her coronation. Her ladies-in-waiting kept her potty handy…?
a) under the table
b) in a room close by
c) on the throne

3 When Anne gave birth to a daughter, Henry…?
a) sulked
b) cheered
c) fell out of his pram

4 While Anne was being beheaded, Henry was playing…?
a) tennis
b) music
c) the fool

5 Henry divorced wife no. 4, Anne of Cleves, because she was…?
a) ugly
b) stupid
c) vegetarian

6 Wife no. 5, Catherine Howard, was sentenced to death for having lovers. She begged for mercy but Heartless Henry locked the door and left her...?

a) to wail

b) in jail

c) looking pale

7 Henry had his old friend Thomas More executed and his head stuck...?

a) over London Bridge

b) under London Bridge

c) in a fridge

8 Henry had Cardinal Fisher beheaded and showed disrespect by leaving the headless body...?

a) naked for a day

b) on the main highway

c) in a window display

INGENIOUS INSULTS

Can you match the words in these columns to come up with ten insults that Shakespeare put into his plays? WARNING: Do NOT call your teacher any of these names.

1 taffeta	**a)** lump
2 scurvy	**b)** ape
3 red-tailed	**c)** chuff
4 threadbare	**d)** bumble-bee
5 mad-headed	**e)** punk
6 fat	**f)** juggler
7 false	**g)** crookback
8 bloodsucker of	**h)** caterpillars
9 scolding	**i)** sleeping men
10 deformed	**j)** lord

QUICK QUIZ – MEAN QUEENS

1 Catholic Mary came to the throne in 1553, and the Protestants showed what they thought of her by leaving something on her bed. What? (Clue: hounding her out of the palace?)

2 Mary married Spanish Prince Philip in 1554. He hated something that came from her nose. What? (Clue: 'snot what you think)

3 Philip left Mary and went to fight in Europe. She tried to tempt him back with what? (Clue: the way to a man's heart is through his stomach, they say)

4 Mary had a lot of Protestant 'heretics' burned. Her chief helper was Reginald Pole who chose really odd 'heretics' to burn. What was odd about them? (Clue: they never felt a thing)

5 Mary sent Archbishop Cranmer to the stake in 1556. He had written an apology then changed his mind. When he saw the fire he did a strange thing. What? (Clue: he went to his death single-handed)

6 Mary died and the news was taken to half-sister Elizabeth, the new queen. They say Elizabeth was reading in the garden when the news came, but that's unlikely. Why? (Clue: remember, remember when Mary died)

7 Elizabeth had a new tax created which only men could pay. It was a tax on what? (Clue: it might grow on you)

8 Elizabeth I's godson, Sir John Harrington, disgraced himself by making rude remarks to her ladies-in-waiting. She banished

him. He went off and invented something that was so useful she forgave him. What? (Clue: flushed with success?)

9 In 1576 the explorer Martin Frobisher returned to England with a load of 'black earth'. What use did he think it would be? (Clue: he thinks the soil is rich)

10 Eloye Mestrell invented the first machine in England for making coins for the government. Yet in 1578 he was arrested and executed. What was his crime? (Clue: double your money)

11 Mary Queen of Scots had Sir John Huntly beheaded but then discovered he had to be tried properly and found guilty if she was to get his fortune. What did she do? (Clue: head on over to the courtroom)

12 Mary Queen of Scots became unpopular in Scotland, and fled to England to ask cousin Elizabeth I for protection. How did Liz protect Mary? (Clue: no one can get in to get her)

13 James Douglas of Scotland invented the 'Maiden' machine. In 1581 the Maiden killed him. What was it? (Clue: a chip off the old block)

14 Mary Queen of Scots had lots of troubles. She finally met a man and thanked him, for 'making an end to all my troubles'. What was this man's job? (Clue: not an agony aunt!)

15 When Mary Queen of Scots was beheaded in 1587 her head was supposed to have been lifted high in the air by the executioner to prove she was dead. But he dropped it. Why? (Clue: hair today, gone tomorrow)

WOULD YOU BELIEVE IT?

Queen Elizabeth I ruled from 1558 to 1603. There are lots of stories about this famous queen, but which of these tall tales are true and which false…?

1 She threatened to pass a law banning her courtiers from wearing long cloaks.

2 She died because of a rotten tooth.

3 Elizabeth was overjoyed when her sister, Mary, died.

4 She liked to read her horoscope.

5 Elizabeth ate a chessboard.

6 She had regular baths.

7 Elizabeth never even considered getting married.

8 Elizabeth had beautiful red hair.

9 She was always true to her Protestant faith.

10 She punched and kicked her secretary.

VILE
VICTORIANS

Quick Victorian Quiz

1 In 1830 the Liverpool to Manchester railway opened. How did Liverpool MP William Huskisson celebrate? (Clue: it's a knockout)

2 In 1831 the north-eastern port of Sunderland brought in a new import. What? (Clue: dis eez a horrible thing to suffer)

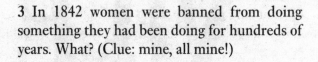

3 In 1842 women were banned from doing something they had been doing for hundreds of years. What? (Clue: mine, all mine!)

4 In 1844 a lady wrote that people were pleased when they smelled bad drains. Why? (Clue: red sky at night)

5 In 1846 a 16-year-old boy was charged with travelling on a train on a 12-year-old's half-price ticket. What was his excuse? (Clue: time to grow)

6 London 'toshers' waded though sewage every day – up to 1.5 metres of the stuff. Why? (Clue: a golden opportunity)

7 In 1847 the Irish were crowding on to 'coffin ships'. Why? (Clue: they've had their chips)

8 In 1848 many European countries were in revolt. The British rebels, the Chartists, had a rally in London but it was a failure. Why? (Clue: it's a wash out)

9 In 1852 in London a small room is opened for men in Fleet Street and they are very relieved! Why? (Clue: gents still use them)

10 In 1853, Australia got stroppy and refused to take any more from Britain. What? (Clue: if they're barred from Australia they'll be barred in Britain)

11 In 1855 Florence Nightingale was nursing Brit soldiers who were fighting the Russians. What happened to their amputated limbs? (Clue: it will make you pig sick)

12 Punching opponents and gouging their eyes was banned in which sport in 1863? (Clue: players put their foot in it)

13 Irish rebels in 1866 invaded which British territory? (Clue: they mountied a successful defence)

14 In 1869 sailors were banned from wearing what? (Clue: it's a close shave)

15 When this man died in 1870 it was said he was 'exhausted by fame'. Who was he? (Clue: no more Christmas Carols)

16 In 1870 a new law forced everyone to do it, even poor little children. What? (Clue: you had to join the class war)

17 In 1879 the Tay Bridge collapsed and a train with almost 100 passengers sank. The bridge inspector had said it was safe. How many bridges had he inspected before? (Clue: not enough)

18 In 1880 the famous writer George Eliot died. What's unusual about him? (Clue: he isn't)

19 SS Daphne was launched on the river Clyde and the workers got a huge surprise. What? (Clue: duck!)

20 In 1888 the police named a murderer even though they never caught him (or her). Who? (Clue: and Jill?)

21 In 1890 a man died. He had been cruelly put on show to the ghoulish public because of his unusual illness. It made him look like what? (Clue: big ears)

22 Copy-cat Blackpool built a copy of the Eiffel Tower in 1894. But is the Blackpool Tower bigger or smaller than the French one? (Clue: it's one or the other!)

23 In 1896 Londoners saw 'Boxing Kangaroos' in Australia. How? (Clue: somebody shot the kangaroos)

24 In 1896 motorists were glad to see the back of a rule that slowed them down. What rule? (Clue: they weren't glad to see the back of this man)

25 In 1899 Percy Pilcher fell 10 metres and was killed. What did he fall from? (Clue: he was hanging around)

26 Queen Victoria's son-in-law, Prince Christian, lost an eye in a shooting accident. At dinner parties he entertained guests with his collection of what? (Clue: quite a sight)

BEHAVE LIKE A VICTORIAN

If a time machine dropped your dad in Victorian London would he act like a gentleman ... or a slob? Test him with these 'do' and 'don't' problems taken from a book of Gentlemen's Manners and see if he could have been accepted by polite Victorians. Just one problem ... if he makes a single mistake he could well be frowned upon for the rest of his life!

Do or don't...
1 offer your hand to an older person to be shaken.
2 eat from the side of your soup spoon and not the end.
3 write to people you know on post cards.
4 remove your overcoat before you enter someone's living room.
5 use slang words.
6 bite into your bread at dinner.
7 call your servants 'girls'.
8 raise your hat to a lady in the street.
9 spit on the pavement.
10 sit with legs crossed.

HOWZAT VICTORIA?

The English lost a cricket match against Australia for the first time in 1880. They burned a bail to ashes and have played for those Ashes ever since. 'How's that?' the cricketers cried (or 'Howzat?' in cricket language) when they thought a batsman was out. And 'Howzat?' is the question about these curious Queen Victoria facts.

1 She was the shortest and the longest reigning monarch Britain ever had! Howzat?

2 Victoria was responsible for the death of her beloved husband, Albert. Howzat?

3 The police set Victoria up as the target for a murdering gunman. Howzat?

4 Victoria was highly respectable all her life yet she caused a scandal in her coffin. Howzat?

5 Albert and Victoria were married in 1840 though he never proposed to her. Howzat?

6 The Victorians liked portrait paintings but she preferred a particular kind. Howzat?

7 Victoria was Queen of England yet the 'Queen's English' was never very good. Howzat?

MANCHESTER MISERY

Not many men in Victorian England were gentlemen– which was unfortunate because gentlemen lived longer than working men. If you were an upper-class person living in Manchester in 1842 youcould expect to live 38 years (on average). But, if you were in the working class what was the average you could expect to live?

a) 37 years, b) 27 years, or c) 17 years

UMMS AND ERRS

The 1800s were the age of the melodrama. Before the days of television the century's soap operas took place in thrilling theatres where villainous Victorians battled against hapless heroes. You just know what they are going to say ... or do you?

1 East Lynne
Poor Isabel leaves her husband but sneaks back (disguised as a governess) to nurse her sickly son. He dies in her arms as Isabel cries...
Oh, Willie, my child! Dead! Dead! Dead! And never called me errrr!

2 A bunch of English soldiers struggle against the enemy who must be evil because they aren't English. (The Victorians could be nasty racists.) Their colonel encourages them...
Remember, Great England is looking at you! Show how her sons can fight and errr!

3 The Fatal Marriage
Poor Isabella loses her husband and marries a dear friend. Then her first husband returns. She tries to murder him then decides to stab herself instead. (Don't try this at home.) Isabella sobs...
When I am dead, forgive me and errr me!

4 The Harp of Altenberg
Our heroine, Innogen, is captured by the villain, Brenno. As she tries to escape he grabs hold of her and Innogen cries...
Errrrme!

5 Sweeney Todd or, The Barber of Fleet Street
Sweeney Todd the Barber cuts the throats of customers and drops the corpses into his cellar. There his next-door neighbour collects the bodies and chops them up to make meat pies. As Sweeney cuts a throat he cries...
I errrrthem off!

6 Maria Marten or, Murder in the Red Barn
Based on a true 1827 murder. William Corder waits in the barn for sweet Maria but plans to shoot her. Corder sneers...
I now await my victim. Will she come? Yes, for women are foolish enough to do anything for the men they errrr!

Even Quicker Victorian Quiz

1 How old were the youngest chimney sweeps in 1804? (Clue: not infants)

2 How was Lord Nelson's body brought home after his death at Trafalgar in 1805? (Clue: not a barrel of laughs)

3 John Bellingham blamed the government for ruining his business. How did he get his revenge in 1812? (Clue: a blow to the head)

4 Napoleon lost the Battle of Waterloo in 1815 What did Brit General Lord Raglan lose? (Clue: 'armless sort of chap)

5 In 1817 Brixton prison invented a new punishment for criminals. What? (Clue: hamster toy)

6 In 1818 Mary Shelley wrote a horrific story that is still popular today. What is it called? (Clue: frankly monstrous)

7 In 1820 in Scotland a rebel weaver was the last man to be sentenced to an ancient punishment. What? (Clue: long and drawn out)

8 In 1821 Queen Caroline died. What did this odd queen put on her head to keep cool while she was out riding? (Clue: American pie)

9 In 1822 King George IV visited Scotland and wore a kilt. How did he keep his knees warm? (Clue: they weren't loose)

10 In 1823 a boy at a public school, William Webb Ellis, cheated at football and invented a new game. What? (Clue: you have to hand it to him)

11 In Edinburgh in 1828 William Blake was accused of 16 murders. What did he do with the bodies? (Clue: they were a little cut up about it)

WOEFUL
SECOND WORLD
WAR

SECOND WORLD WAR WONDERS

Try this quick quiz on the Second World War. Replace the words 'Laurel and Hardy'* with one of the answers below. One of those answers is 'Laurel and Hardy'!

The missing words in the wrong order are: uniforms, 16-year-old boys, Laurel and Hardy, bonfires, nuns, toilet rolls, women, prison, parachutes, guillotines.

1 British and Allied troops coloured everything khaki brown as camouflage. They even had khaki Laurel and Hardy.

2 The British Home Guard were warned that an enemy paratrooper might be disguised as Laurel and Hardy.

3 Some spies in Germany were executed by Laurel and Hardy.

4 British soldiers in Italy were given summer Laurel and Hardy and some died of the cold.

5 In November 1940 a man called Lloyd was arrested in Britain for having Laurel and Hardy in his back garden.

6 US paratroopers were safer than British ones because they had two Laurel and Hardy.

7 The Germans sent Laurel and Hardy into battle when they became short of soldiers.

8 The Nazis thought ideal Laurel and Hardy should have broad hips.

* If you're not old enough to know who Laurel and Hardy are, then ask your teacher or a parent.

9 Workers who were late for work in a German factory ended up in Laurel and Hardy.

10 Italian leader Mussolini was said to look like one half of Laurel and Hardy.

WELL THIS WAR IS CERTAINLY KEEPING US BUSY OLLIE!

QUICK SECOND WORLD WAR QUIZ

1 When the Second World War started in 1939 civilians were urged to join the Local Defence Volunteers. Comedians said LDV stood for Look, Duck and … what? (Clue: vanquish? Not quite)

2 In May 1940 Mr Hitler did something a certain Mr Fawkes failed to do. What? (Clue: remember?)

3 In 1940 a man was arrested for lighting a cigarette. Why? (Clue: night-light)

4 The British government tried to ban Londoners sheltering in the Underground stations during bombing raids. What did the crafty Cockneys do? (Clue: train for it)

5 Car headlights were masked because of the blackout. How did farmers protect their black cattle that may have strayed on to the road? (Clue: zebra crossing?)

6 Why did parents have to label every piece of their children's clothing during the war? (Clue: bits and pieces)

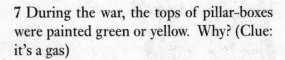

7 During the war, the tops of pillar-boxes were painted green or yellow. Why? (Clue: it's a gas)

8 When the war ended in 1945 some children tried to eat bananas without peeling them. Why? (Clue: Yes! We have no bananas!)

9 In the 1940s you could eat 'chicken fruit on bacon ducks'. What was it?
a) boiled beef and carrots
b) omelette with sun dried tomatoes
c) eggs on fried bread

10 During the Second World War, US soldiers were advised to eat…
a) caterpillars
b) maggots
c) absolutely anything

MORE CATERPILLAR CASSEROLE PLEASE

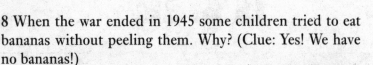

WAR-LIKE WORDS?

At the end of the millennium, people were still bombing and killing but they'd found some new words to describe it so that it sounded less horrible. See if you can work out what these military phrases mean.

Words	Meaning
1 air support	a) human beings
2 friendly fire	b) destroy
3 neutralizing	c) planes dropping bombs
4 soft targets	d) blowing people to pieces by mistake
5 collateral damage	e) assassinating a human nuisance
6 immobilize	f) shooting soldiers on your own side

THESE DAYS YOU NEED GUNS, TANKS, SMART BOMBS AND A DICTIONARY

AWESOME
ANSWERS

SAVAGE STONE AGE

(pages 5–10)

Horrible Hominid Habits
1b) 2a) 3a) 4b) 5c) 6a) 7b) 8a)

Extraordinary Evidence

1 TRUE. Tooth drills made of flint have been found in Pakistan that date from 9,000 years ago!

2 FALSE. They lived and moved about in groups.

3 FALSE. Dinosaurs had died out long before early humans walked the Earth.

4 TRUE. Stone razors have been discovered that date from 30,000 BC.

5 TRUE.

6 FALSE. They worshipped the spirits of their dead ancestors.

7 TRUE.

8 TRUE. Some sick scientists believe they ate the brains!

Awful Ancestors and Rotten Relations
1f) 2d) 3h) 4a) 5g) 6e) 7c) 8b) (actually, that's a bit of a swizz – the rudolfensis part comes from Lake Rudolf, which is where this horrible hominid was discovered and what Lake Turkana used to be called)

The Loopy Leakeys
1 SAND HUB = HUSBAND
2 SULLK = SKULL
3 MANUH = HUMAN
4 PEA = APE
5 ACE SNORT = ANCESTOR

6 FROSTPOINT = FOOTPRINTS
7 VANCOLIC = VOLCANIC
8 GIRTH UP = UPRIGHT
9 SCOREDIVED = DISCOVERED
10 SHY RIOT = HISTORY

AWFUL EGYPTIANS
(pages 11–26)
Extraordinary Ancient Egypt
1a) 2b) 3a) 4b) 5c) 6c) 7a) 8b)

Groovy Gods
1g) 2d) 3a) 4h) 5c) 6b) 7f) 8e)

Egyptian Fact or Fiction
1 TRUE. Ancient Egyptian workers went on strike because they weren't paid on time. And they weren't even holding out for cash – they were paid in bags of corn!
2 FALSE. The awful Egyptians hacked off the HANDS of their enemies so they knew how many they had killed.
3 TRUE. Basic scissors have been found in ancient Egyptian ruins. They weren't particularly good because they were made from a single piece of metal (it was the ruthless Romans who thought it would be a better idea to have two separate blades).
4 TRUE. This probably didn't work, but at least it gave the sufferer something to suck on.
5 TRUE. But no one knows for sure why or how they were killed.
6 FALSE. They didn't invent toffee apples, but the ancient Egyptians were the first people to make marshmallows, from

the roots of – yes, you guessed it – the marshmallow plant!

7 FALSE. The men who built the pyramids weren't slaves – they were paid workers. Aha – a trick question! Mean. It still took 25,000 of them five years to build one, though…

8 TRUE. This might explain why the Egyptians were often beaten in battle…

Barmy Embalming
1g) 2b) 3e) 4a) 5f) 6c) 7h) 8d)

Phascinating Pharaoh Phacts
1 At Giza. It's the largest pyramid in Egypt.
2 The embalmers stuffed peppercorns up his nose to give it its shape back.
3 He built his pyramid as a maze of twisting tunnels and dead ends.
4 She would often wear a weird beard. I don't suppose anyone was fooled…
5 He had their ears cut off.
6 He had the longest reign of any ancient Egyptian pharaoh.
7 He married his own daughter, Satamum. But that wasn't as bad as Ramesses II, who married three of his own daughters!
8 He hacked off their heads.

Gruesome Gods
These are the unscrabbled words in the story: magnificent; organised; festivities; announced; sealed; searched; burial; angered (or enraged!); scattered; reassembled.

Wrotten Writing
Did you decipher?: My nits ar itchy

Potty Pyramids

All except **3** have been believed by someone … usually someone with more thumbnail than brain, but you can believe them if you like. Most people just admit they are huge tombs for dead kings.

Quick Egyptian Quiz:

1 Animal droppings. Poo! Imagine if your house was made of mud mixed with animal droppings! (Maybe it is!) And imagine mixing it in the days before rubber gloves had been invented. The Egyptians also burned animal droppings to make a fire.

2 Mummified cats. The cats had their necks broken, then were wrapped like a pharaoh's mummy. Pilgrims offered the cats to the gods. Vast cemeteries have been discovered with many thousands of these cat burials. It is likely that the animals were specially bred for this purpose. By 1900 hundreds of tonnes of mummified cats had been shipped to Liverpool to be ground up and used as fertilizer.

Horrible Histories note: Some school books tell you the Egyptians turned their cats to mummies because they loved their cute little kitties so much! Nice idea – load of rubbish.

3 He was beaten. Miss a day's work, weaver, and you get fifty lashes. And weaving was a tough job – you worked all day with your knees drawn up to your chest.

4 To keep free of lice. Everyone from pharaoh to peasant suffered from lice in the hair. Priests became slapheads to keep clean.

5 A turtle. It was not a common statue in Egypt so Horemheb probably had to shell out a lot of money to buy it!

6 Mud. The early Egyptians called themselves 'black-landers' because they believed they were made from the dark, rich soil by the River Nile. Khnum, they said, breathed life into them and the mud became human beings. Muddy marvellous!

7 With a herd of sheep, goats or pigs. These herds ran around the field and trampled in the grain. Don't try this at home.

8 They used children as scarecrows. Nowadays we'd probably use traffic wardens because they are scarier than anything.

9 He had to run around his palace. Some historians believe that in the early days of Egypt, if the king failed the test he would be sacrificed. He was literally running for his life!

10 Two. An in-side and an out-side. (Oh, come on! This is a Horrible Histories book! What did you expect? A fair question?)

ROTTEN ROMANS

(pages 27–36)

Evil Emperors

1 Head. Nice present for Jules!

2 Leg. Tiberius died at the age of 78, probably suffocated by his chief helper.

3 Horse. Cruel Caligula liked to feed criminals to wild animals. He was stabbed to death by one of his guards.

4 Wife. She was a bit of a flirt. But he also had 300 of her party friends chopped too! His third wife, and niece, had him poisoned with mushrooms.

5 Mother. When the plot failed he sent soldiers to give her the chop. Nero stabbed himself to death before his enemies got to him.

6 Corpse. He was murdered in the centre of Rome but not given a nice emperor's burial.

7 Wrinkly. Hadrian accused Servianus of treason and forced him to kill himself. But Servianus was 90 years old and hardly a big threat.

8 Cheese. At least that's what a Roman historian blamed his death on. Guess it was just hard cheese.

9 Cobweb. Maybe he was planning to build the world's first web-site?

10 Chicken. Trouble is he loved the chicken Rome more than he loved the city Rome, and the city was neglected.

Stabbing Jules

These are the unscrabbled words in the correct order: signal; knife; Caesar's; watchers; assassin; beast; trusted; statue; blood; wounded

Foul Roman Food

1b) The guts were soaked in salt water and left to stew in the sun for a few days. Then the fish-gut sauce was poured over the food as a tasty treat. Oh my cod!

2a) They went to a special room called a vomitorium and threw up. They used a stick with a feather to tickle their tonsils and vomited into a bowl. When their stomach was empty they went back and ate more. Scoff-vomit, scoff-vomit, scoff-vomit all night long. Good idea for school dinners?

3c) The snails supped the blood till they were too fat to get in their shells. The blood diet made them taste nice. If they wanted creamy snails, the Romans fed them on milk before eating them.

4c) Eliogabalus mixed gold and precious stones with the peas as a sort of treat. But if one of those diamonds smashed your teeth you'd be sore. And if you swallowed a gold nugget you'd be ill! You'd have to sit on the toilet and wait for some change!

5a) Ostrich brains are quite small so he'd need 600 to keep his guests fed. But where did he get all those ostriches? Zoo knows?

6b) There were thrushes stuffed inside the roast boar. (Were they bored in there?) Trimalchio also served wine that was 100 years old at that feast.

7b) Of course, the trouble with gladiators fighting as you eat is that they could splash blood and guts all over your freshly cooked dinner. Aren't you lucky you don't suffer that while you watch telly?

8c) They fed the dormice really well on walnuts, acorns and chestnuts. They were served roasted and stuffed with pork sausage. Scrummy! Even tastier than hamster or gerbil!

9a) They ate all sorts of other things though. As well as sheep and goat lungs or brains, they ate gulls, peacocks, swans and jackdaws. They stuffed the birds just by pushing stuffing straight down their throats. They didn't clean the insides out the way you do with your Christmas turkey. Yeuch!

10c) That's about a small sheep every day. Would ewe believe it? He was also supposed to have drunk about 34 litres of wine … but it must have been very weak. Of course, after 20 years all that eating killed him, but he was probably too drunk to notice he was dead!

Awful army

1c) You have to fight for Rome, which is a real pain in the neck. If you don't it's a real pain in the neck.

2c) Can you blame them? Go to Hadrian's Wall in winter and see how cold it gets. You'd want to wear five pairs of knickers!

3c) Paying for your own burial is a bit tough. If I were a dead Roman soldier I'd refuse to pay!

4b) Unless you were killed, of course, in which case you were in it for life!

5b) The sponge was dipped in water (cold), used, then rinsed and left for the next person. Hmmm! Try it next time you run out of a roll.

6a) At least, they weren't supposed to marry. But many soldiers had wives outside the camp.

7b) But this rule was often broken if the army was desperate for men. Of course, if you wanted to dodge the army you could cut off your head and you'd probably be too short! (*Horrible Histories* are full of cool ideas like that!)

8b) The idea was that they hit their enemy. But if they missed and the head snapped off, then the enemy couldn't throw them back.

Gory gladiators

1 entertainment; 2 butchery; 3 swords; 4 lions; 5 winners; 6 death; 7 spectators; 8 robbers; 9 murderers; 10 sport.

Quick Roman quiz

1 He burned them alive. Rome had seven fire brigades and they all failed to control the Great Fire. They also failed to put out the burning Christians. The firemen also acted as sort of night-watch policemen. With two jobs, up all night, they were probably too sleepy to notice the Great Fire!

2 They were all buried outside the city. Julius Caesar passed a law saying cremations and burials must take place outside the city. This was to keep diseases out of the city. Well, you wouldn't want a mouldy body in your back garden, would you?

3 The pig's stomach. They knotted it at each end, then blew it up. Would you fancy giving a kiss of life to a pig's belly? They played ball games like 'trigon' – rather like passing a balloon between three people.

4 With a hammer blow to the head. This was cleaner than a chop with a sword. After all, these servants had to keep sprinkling sand in the arenas to soak up the blood and stop fresh gladiators slipping. So a hammer-smack saved on sand!

5 The spider's web. And crushed frogs drunk in wine are a good cure for toad-poison. It's no worse than some things you eat in burger bars.

6 His eyes fell out. At least that's what the legend says. But it may just be true, so don't go around lopping off saintly heads – unless you want a real close-up view of your shoelaces.

7 They were crucified. No one is quite sure if Spartacus was crucified or died in battle. But it's a great story that has been turned into books and films and computer games and even a ballet. (No, it was a modern computer game, not a Roman computer game, dummy!)

8 The fans. Just like modern soccer matches the fans had

their favourites and the real boneheads wanted to give rival fans a kicking. Not a lot has changed in 2,000 years, has it?

Measly Middle Ages

(pages 37–42)

Middle Ages Mind-benders

1 Wedding guests threw sawdust over the brides. (If you go to a wedding today then you might throw confetti over the bride for luck. In the Middle Ages the guests threw sawdust.)

2 Students were not allowed to stab their teachers. (It was forbidden to knife an examiner just because he asked you a hard question!)

3 A rider and his horse drowned in a hole in the road. (A miller dug clay from the middle of the road to mend his house. The hole filled with water after a storm and a travelling glove-maker fell in and drowned— along with his horse.)

4 A giant used his single foot as an umbrella. (Superstitious people believed in monsters, such as the one-legged 'Sciapod'. He lay on his back stuck his leg in the air and sheltered under the shadow of his huge foot.)

5 The Count of Armagnac broke his wife's bones in a row. (He was trying to persuade her to sign over some land. After beating her he threw her in a dungeon. This was gentle persuasion.)

6 A panter looked after the castle pantry. (He could have been named after the place where he worked – or he could have been a panter because he had to run up and down all those castle stairs!)

7 Rebel Wat Tyler's proper name was Walter. (He could have been called a Wally.)

8 Teachers at St Paul's school collected the boys' pee in a barrel. (It was sold to leather workers to soften the leather. So if your shoes are hard and uncomfortable, you know what to do? Limp.)

9 Monks polished their heads with a stone. (It was a stone called a 'pumice'. The slaphead monks would have used sandpaper if it had been invented.)

10 Dick Whittington was twice mayor of Calais. (Dick Whittington was a real person. Everyone knows the story of Dick and his cat and the bells that said, 'Turn again Whittington and you shall be Lord Mayor of London three times.' BUT not a lot of people know that he was also mayor of Calais – twice!

Clueless Cures
1–19 ALL are true except **3** (a cure for toothache), **5** (a cure for a headache) and **8** (a cure for a cough).

Weird Words
1 Thin; **2** Hood; **3** Hair; **4** Shoes; **5** Toes; **6** Rags; **7** Filth; **8** Ankles; **9** Oxen; **10** Ribs

Quick Middle Ages Quiz
1 Prince of Wales. It's a title that has been given to an English monarch's oldest son ever since.

2 Ed rode out and took on the outlaw in a fight. He beat him and made the road safe. (This is probably not a true story, though)

3 His soldiers disguised themselves as cattle! Under the cover of the skins they got close enough to surprise the guards.

4 116 years.

5 Richard collapsed under the strain of the excitement – and the heavy robes and crown.

6 A skin! He was supposed to have been wrapped in a goat skin to save his life! Weird.

7 Wat.

8 The Handkerchief.

9 He starved himself to death, some said. Others said he'd been starved on the orders of the king.

10 Catherine's corpse was turned into a mummy and put on show next to the coffin of Henry V. People could look at her for a couple of pennies and she stayed there for almost 300 years. Samuel Pepys kissed the mummy— weird!

11 Henry sat on him mum's knee. He was just eight months old when he took the throne. Some days he had such screaming fits that his visits to parliament had to be cancelled.

TERRIBLE TUDORS
(pages 43–52)
Quick Tudor Quiz

1 Margaret's sister died at the same time. It's a fair bet they were both poisoned. James went on to marry Henry VIII's sister instead.

2 Henry VII (who died in 1509) and also his eldest son, Arthur (who died in 1502).

3 He was 70. The oldest Scot in battle, William Maitland, actually fought and died – and he was 90!

4 Catherine sent the bloodstained coat from the dead King of Scotland. Henry was furious. He wanted the glory of the victory for himself. There's no pleasing some people.

5 Patrick Hamilton was burned to death but the damp

weather meant he burnt slowly. The executioners tried to put gunpowder on the fire but that only scorched him.

6 Henry ordered that Rosse be boiled alive in his own pot. Rosse always said that he put the poison in the pot as a joke – it wasn't meant to kill.

7 She was hanged along with three men who supported her attack on the king.

8 Very short. He asked the executioner to try and be an accurate shot with the axe.

9 They were all called 'Catherine'.

10 Anne wasn't beheaded on a block. She knelt down and her head was removed with a single swipe of a sword. It was said her lips kept moving in prayer for minutes after her head was off.

11 Henry tried to put it off until he could find an excuse not to do it. He didn't want to marry Anne after all, but he knew if he refused he would upset her powerful father. In the end he had to go ahead.

12 James didn't turn up. James' councillors said Henry was planning a trap.

13 She moved her head around to make the job as difficult as possible for the executioner. It took him several chops at her shoulders before he finally hit her neck and got her head off.

14 Lady Rochford arranged the meetings between Catherine and her boyfriends.

15 Rolled over and sank. It may have been top heavy with guns and men and the boat was upset. Henry was upset too – but 500 people on board were dead upset. Simply dead, in fact.

16 It was illegal for anyone to say, 'The king is going to die.' So they didn't say it – but he died anyway.

17 Henry had died three days earlier on 28 January. The

lords wanted his death kept secret for a few days till the throne was safe for Edward VI to take it. They had meals delivered to the room to make it seem normal. But who ate them?

18 She had him burned. Probably not true.

19 The dog was shot dead by the visitor, who was Ed's uncle. He was executed, and the mutt was avenged.

Awful Aztecs

1 FALSE. They had armour but it was made of hardened cotton.

2 TRUE. The knives were made from a type of natural glass called 'obsidian'.

3 TRUE. They were given a loincloth, shield, cloak and four arrows when they were a few days old.

4 TRUE. They believed they would hum off to join the Sun God.

5 TRUE. And the human manure would be used as fertilizer for crops.

6 FALSE. Warriors couldn't get their hair cut until they'd killed someone in battle.

7 TRUE. Lake scum was made into cakes.

8 FALSE. He had to ask his teacher!

9 TRUE.

10 FALSE. The Spanish brought diseases from Europe which killed many Aztecs.

Horrible Henry

1–8. All answers are (a). Anyone answering (c) should give up quizzes ... now.

Ingenious insults

1e) 2j) 3d) 4f) 5b) 6c) 7h) 8i) 9g) 10a)

1 A dead dog. The head was shaved, the ears cropped and a noose put around its neck. The message was clear: 'This is what we do to Catholics.'

2 Philip hated Mary's foul breath. It was an illness she had and not her fault. But it put him off, and he left her broken hearted.

3 His favourite meat pies. She had them sent across the English Channel to him. He ate all the pies but didn't go home for more.

4 They were dead. Reggie dug them up and burned them anyway. Funny feller.

5 He stuck his writing hand in the flames to punish it for writing the apology. (No jokes about second-hand shops, please.)

6 It was November. Not many people are daft enough to sit in the garden in an English winter.

7 Beards.

8 A flushing toilet. It took him six years to invent it but Liz loved his loo.

9 He believed it contained a fortune in gold. It didn't. He was just a clueless captain.

10 Eloye made a second, secret, machine and forged money for himself. Usually forgers had a hand chopped off but Eloye was hanged.

11 Huntly's head was sewn back on and his corpse was put on trial.

12 Elizabeth locked Mary in prison. She left her there for years before deciding to execute her.

13 The Maiden was a type of guillotine. He was executed on it.

14 He was her executioner. Actually he made a messy end to her troubles, taking three chops and a bit of sawing to get the head off

15 Mary was wearing a wig. When he grabbed it, the head slipped out and bounced on to the floor.

Would you believe it?
1 TRUE. She was terrified of being killed and wanted her courtiers' swords uncovered and ready.
2 FALSE. Elizabeth is famous for having rotten teeth, but that didn't kill her. She caught a cold and never recovered.
3 TRUE. She said, 'This is the Lord's doing and it is marvellous in our eyes.'
4 TRUE. A mathematician (and magician!) called John Dee used to read Liz's horoscope and foretell the future for her.
5 TRUE. Of course, it was made of marzipan.
6 TRUE. Elizabeth did bathe regularly ... once every three months!
7 FALSE. Liz had a few close calls when it came to marriage, including Lord Dudley and the French Duke of Anjou.
8 TRUE *and* FALSE. She did at first, but she ended up bald with a collection of 80 wigs!
9 FALSE. While Catholic Mary Tudor was queen, Elizabeth said she was a Catholic too.
10 TRUE. Secretary William Davison was just one of the unfortunate palace workers who suffered Liz's temper tantrums.

VILE VICTORIANS
(pages 53–62)
Quick Victorian Quiz
1 Huskisson stepped from his carriage to say hello to friends, was hit by a train and died.
2 The disease of cholera. Not only does it give you disgusting diarrhoea but victims turn blue before they die. 20,000 died

in the next year.

3 Women (and boys under 10) were no longer allowed to work in mines. They lost their wages so it isn't all good news.

4 It was a sign of bad weather on the way. People were glad of the warning. Modern weather forecasts smell better.

5 'The train's so slow, I was 12 when I got on it.' On most lines 30 mph was thought to be quite fast enough.

6 They were looking for coins and metal dropped through drains. Would you stick your hand down a toilet for your pocket money? Toshers would.

7 They were emigrating from Ireland because they were starving in the potato famine. The old ships, nicknamed coffin ships, didn't always make it. Starve or drown? Some choice.

8 It rained heavily and many people stayed at home rather than get wet.

9 It was the first flushing public toilet for men – but not women, who would have to keep their legs crossed!

10 Convicts. Australia was a dumping ground for Brit criminals and now it stopped. Brit criminals got harsher sentences at home instead and no kangaroo steaks.

11 They were dumped outside the hospital and eaten by pigs. Then the pigs were eaten by the patients ... including the patients who lost arms and legs. You could say they ended up eating themselves! Yeuch!

12 Soccer. The new rules said that only the goalkeeper could handle the ball. It also banned fighting on the pitch. Someone should tell today's players!

13 Canada! Yes it sounds odd but with the help of US troops the Irish rebels attacked Brit troops in Canada as the first stage of attacking Brit troops in Ireland.

14 Moustaches. Sailors could be clean shaven or wear beards, but moustaches were popular with soldiers and the navy didn't want its men to look like their great rivals in the army!

15 Charles Dickens. He was only 58 but was racing around the country, reading and acting his characters. It killed him.

16 Go to school. The Education Reform Act forced everyone to suffer at school whether they liked it or not.

17 None. The inspector wasn't trained and had never inspected a bridge before. He wouldn't have known a bad bridge if it had jumped up and bitten him on the nose.

18 George Eliot was a woman, real name Mary Anne Evans. She didn't think publishers would print a book by a woman so she lied and said she was a man.

19 The ship slid into the river, rolled over and drowned 124 of them. Well, they built it, so they couldn't complain – and they didn't.

20 Jack the Ripper. He killed eight women and the mystery has never been forgotten – or solved. But Queen Victoria showed an unusual interest in the case. Hmmmm!

21 An elephant. Joseph Merrick was known as the Elephant Man and he was treated as a freak, rather than a sick person. He died aged just 27.

22 Smaller. Blackpool Tower is only half the height of the Eiffel Tower – but people falling off the top end up with exactly the same amount of deadness.

23 The kangaroos were in the first cinema show in Britain. Now you know the answer you'll be hoppy.

24 Motorists were now allowed to drive without being led by a man with a red flag. The speed limit also went up from 4 mph to 20 mph. Scary!

25 An early hang glider.

26 Glass eyes. His favourite was a bloodshot eye which he used when he had a cold!

Behave like a Victorian

1 Don't. Wait until they have offered it to you.

2 Do. And remember you mustn't gurgle or suck in your breath while you sip your soup.

3 Don't. Write letters or nothing at all.

4 Do. Even if it's only a very short call.

5 Don't. Well, usually. There are some slang words that a gentleman may use. If you don't know what they are then avoid slang altogether.

6 Don't. Break off a piece and place it in your mouth.

7 Don't. Call them maids or servants.

8 Do. BUT ... wait till she has bowed to you first and do not wave your hat in the air the way the French do – put it straight back on to your head.

9 Don't. Or anywhere else for that matter!

10 Don't. The book admits that most men do this but says it is extremely impolite.

Howzat Victoria?

1 She was the shortest in height but the longest in the time she spent on the throne.

2 The dirty water from her toilet leaked into Albert's drinking water and gave him the disease that killed him.

3 The gunman tried to shoot her as she drove in her carriage in London. His gun misfired and he escaped. The police told her to drive in the same place and at the same time the next day so that he could try again. He did! They caught him.

4 She was buried with a photograph of her 'friend', her Scottish servant. In her hand was a lock of his hair. What had they been up to when she was alive, people wanted to know!

5 Victoria proposed to him!

6 Victoria (and hubby Albert) preferred the people in the pictures to have no clothes on!

7 She was from the German Hanover family so she always spoke with a German accent.

Manchester Misery

c) In London slums people would, on average, live 22 years – but average upper class people would live twice as long. The unhealthiest place to live in 1842 was Liverpool, where the average age of death was just 15 years old. Queen Victoria lived to be 81. The average age was so low because lots of children died very young.

Umms and Errs

1 Mother. 'On the telephone' is definitely wrong! So is 'a taxi'.

2 Die. 'Fight and win' would not be very English – lookat the present-day cricket team.

3 Pity. 'Bury' makes a bit more sense, you have to admit.

4 Unhand. Not a word you'll hear very often but remember it next time a history teacher grabs you!

5 Polish. This is such a famous line your granny probably knows it. In fact she probably ate the pies!

6 Love. 'Get chocolates from' is not a good enough answer.

Even Quicker Victorian Quiz

1 Four years old. The sweeps weren't supposed to be under nine but employers lied about the ages of their workers.

2 Pickled in a barrel of brandy. It preserved the body – and the sailors drank the brandy afterwards!

3 He shot the Prime Minister, Spencer Perceval, dead. The only Brit PM to be assassinated. Bellingham was hanged.

4 His arm. He also almost lost his wedding ring when the arm was amputated. 'Here! Bring that arm back!' he cried from his hospital bed.

5 The 'treadmill'– a bit like a hamster wheel, where the prisoners walk and walk and go nowhere.

6 Frankenstein. Monstrous Mary was only 18 when she dreamed up this story of a man put together like a Lego kit. Seriously weird writer.

7 Wilson was sentenced to be hanged, drawn and quartered. In fact he was hanged then beheaded. His 'crime' was to lead a march in protest against unemployment.

8 A pumpkin. She probably changed it each time she rode, which is more than she did with her stockings. She wore them till they stank.

9 Tights. He had them made the colour of his flesh because he didn't want to look like a wimp.

10 Rugby. He picked up the ball and ran with it. The game was named after his public school, Rugby, so we don't say, 'Fancy a game of Ellis?'

11 He sold them to doctors so they could experiment on them. Of course the doctors weren't punished.

WOEFUL SECOND WORLD WAR

(pages 63–67)

Second World War Wonders

1 Toilet rolls. A quick flash of white could give them away to the enemy!

2 Nuns. Or vicars or a woman carrying a baby.

3 Guillotines. In August 1942 German spy-catchers uncovered a team of 46 spies. The male spies were hanged, but for some reason the female spies were guillotined.

4 Uniforms. The army planners believed it would be very

hot in Italy, but it was wet and cold and in the mountains it was freezing.

5 Bonfires. Mr Lloyd supported the Nazi party. The magistrate gave Lloyd a prison sentence – Lloyd gave the magistrate a Nazi salute.

6 Parachutes. The British Army said two parachutes took up too much room. The truth was probably that it would have been too expensive.

7 16-year-old boys. As the war went on and the fit men were killed or captured the German Army called for older men and younger boys to join.

8 Women. The ideal Nazi woman should also have blonde hair, never wear make-up or trousers, and wear her hair in a bun or plaits.

9 Prison. You could be sentenced to three months in prison. (And you thought an hour's detention for being late to school was cruel!)

10 Laurel and Hardy. Mussolini was short and fat. When he became ruler of Italy he wore a dark suit and a bowler hat. Somebody told him he looked just like Oliver Hardy – a comic idiot – so he began dressing in military uniforms instead.

Quick Second World War Quiz
1 Vanish. The LDV went on to become the Home Guard, popularly known as 'Dad's Army'.

2 His bombs flattened the Houses of Parliament.

3 He was breaking the blackout laws in force during the war.

4 They bought platform tickets so no one could stop them going down to safety.

5 They painted white stripes down their sides.

6 If the child was blown to pieces then the bits could be identified. Gruesome but true-some.

7 So that droplets of deadly mustard gas would stain the paint and show if there was a gas attack.

8 Many children had never seen a banana and didn't know what to do with it.

9c)

10b) A US Army handbook advised them to eat maggots and grasshoppers (with the wings and legs removed!), but advised against eating caterpillars.

War-like words
1c) 2f) 3e) 4a) 5d) 6b)

Terry Deary was born at a very early age, so long ago he can't remember. But his mother, who was there at the time, says he was born in Sunderland, north-east England, in 1946 – so it's not true that he writes all *Horrible Histories* from memory. At school he was a horrible child only interested in playing football and giving teachers a hard time. His history lessons were so boring and so badly taught, that he learned to loathe the subject. *Horrible Histories* is his revenge.

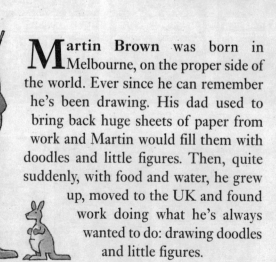

Martin Brown was born in Melbourne, on the proper side of the world. Ever since he can remember he's been drawing. His dad used to bring back huge sheets of paper from work and Martin would fill them with doodles and little figures. Then, quite suddenly, with food and water, he grew up, moved to the UK and found work doing what he's always wanted to do: drawing doodles and little figures.

Make sure you've got the whole horrible lot!